The First Christmas

Long ago, in a town called
Nazareth, there lived a young
woman named Mary. One day
a great light appeared and
the angel Gabriel stood before her.
"Do not be afraid," said the angel.
"I bring you joyful news.
God has chosen you to be
the mother of his son. You will
have a baby and you must
call him Jesus."

Designed by Brigitte Willgoss

This book belongs to

....

ISBN 0 86112 630 0
Published by Brimax Books Ltd, Newmarket, England 1989.
Produced by Mandarin Offset
Printed and bound in Hong Kong

My first
Christmas
Storybook

By Greg Steddy

Illustrated by Cathie Shuttleworth

Brimax Books · Newmarket · England

In the same town there lived
a carpenter named Joseph.
Joseph loved Mary very much.
He was going to marry her.
The angel came to visit Joseph
and told him that Mary was going
to have God's son. Later that day
Joseph came to see Mary and told
her what the angel had said.

One day a message came from
the governor of the land.
All of the people had to go back
to the place where they had been
born so they could be counted.
Joseph was worried. He and Mary
would have to go to Bethlehem.
This was a long way away
and Mary was almost ready
to have her baby.

They set off early the next morning. Joseph led the way. Mary rode on a donkey. The road was long and hard. They didn't reach Bethlehem until the evening. The town was full of people. Joseph tried everywhere to find a place to stay, but all the rooms were taken. Mary was so tired she could hardly stay awake.

At last an innkeeper said,
"All my rooms are full, but you
can use my stable. It is clean
and warm in there."
Joseph thanked him and they went
inside. All around them cows and
donkeys lay peacefully asleep.
The hay was soft and smelled sweet.
Mary and Joseph lay down and rested.

In the night, Mary gave birth to
her baby. It was a boy as
the angel had said. They named
him Jesus.
Mary wrapped him in a blanket
and laid him in a manger, where
it was soft and warm.
Mary and Joseph watched over
Jesus lovingly. They knew he was
a very special baby.

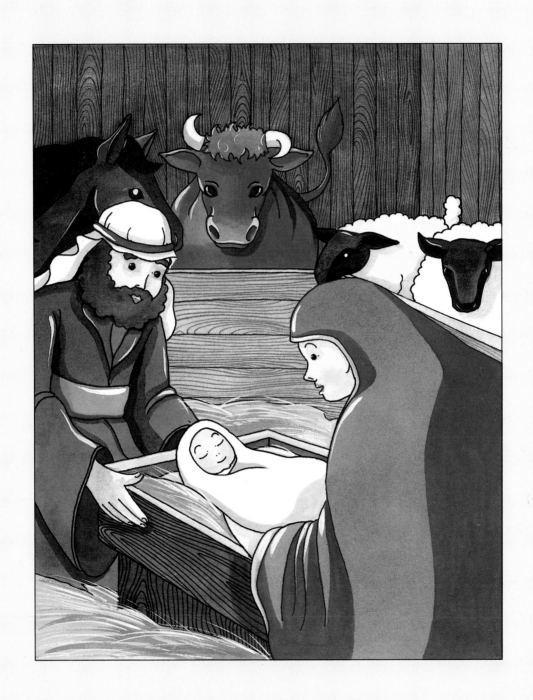

Out on the hillside above
the town, some shepherds were
looking after their sheep.
Suddenly the sky was filled with
light and an angel appeared.
The shepherds fell to the ground
in fear.
But the angel said, "Do not be
afraid. I bring you good news.
Today a child is born. He is the
son of God. You will find him in
Bethlehem, lying in a manger."

The shepherds gazed in wonder
as the sky was filled with angels
singing.
"We must go and find this child,"
said one. "We can take one of our
newborn lambs as a gift."
They went to Bethlehem and found
Jesus in the stable with Mary and
Joseph. They fell to their knees
and offered their gift.

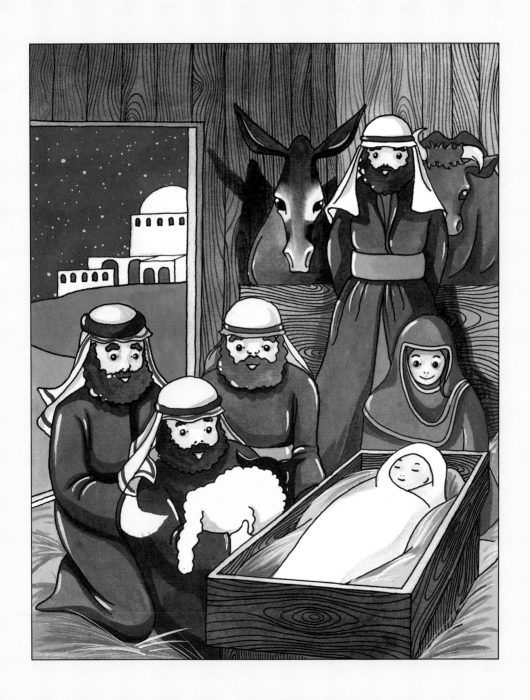

Far away in an eastern land
lived three wise men. One night
they saw a bright new star in
the sky. They wanted to know
what it meant. They looked in
their books for the answer.
"It means that a new king
has been born," they said.
"We must go and look for him
so that we can worship him.
The star will guide us."

25

They set off on their journey.
The star shone brightly in front
of them by day and by night.
They came to the palace of King
Herod. He was not very pleased
when he heard about the new king.
"Go and find him, so that
I can worship him, too," said Herod.
He really wanted to find Jesus
so that he could kill him.

The three wise men followed
the star for many miles.
It stopped right over the stable
where Jesus lay. "We are looking
for the newborn king," they said.
"A bright star has guided us
from far away."
Joseph led them into the stable.
They knelt before Jesus and
offered him some very special
gifts of gold, frankincense
and myrrh.

The next day, the wise men set out for King Herod's palace. They stopped to rest and while they were asleep an angel came to them in a dream.
"Do not go back to Herod," the angel warned. "He wants to kill Jesus."
The wise men decided to go home a different way.

Mary and Joseph were very happy and proud. They knew their baby was really the son of God. They knew he was very special and that he would have important work to do when he grew up. They also knew that Jesus would be loved throughout the world and that people would remember his birth as a time of happiness and peace.

Say these words again

town

angel

carpenter

God

message

tired

find

full

stable

baby

manger

singing

lamb

gold

Who can you see?

Mary

Jesus

Joseph

shepherd

wisemen

Santa Claus

It was Christmas Eve. At the North Pole, where Santa Claus lives, everyone was very busy. For weeks the elves had been hard at work. They had made and wrapped up hundreds of presents for Santa to deliver. There were presents everywhere, of all shapes and sizes. Each was wrapped in bright paper. It was a wonderful sight.

Outside, Santa's sleigh was
almost ready for his journey
around the world.
The elves had given it a new
coat of paint and it shone
in the winter sunshine.
In the stables were six fine
reindeer. They had all had their
coats washed and brushed. Even
their antlers had been polished,
ready for their great ride
through the night.

At last it was time to load
the presents onto the sleigh.
The elves worked hard all
afternoon until the sleigh was
piled high. It was so full of
presents that there was barely
enough room for Santa to sit!
The reindeer were brought out
and one by one they were tied
to the front of the sleigh. The bells
on their bridles jingled merrily.

Finally Santa Claus arrived.
He was dressed in red.
"Well done, my friends!" he said.
"Everything looks splendid!"
He patted each of the reindeer.
Then he sprinkled them with magic
dust so that they could fly.
"Away we go!" he cried.
The sleigh began to rise slowly
into the dark night air.

They hadn't gone far when it
began to snow. The snow got thicker
and thicker. Soon they could
hardly see where they were going.
"That looks like a rooftop down
there!" cried Santa, peering
through the swirling snow.
The reindeer flew downward
and landed with a bump. They
hadn't landed on a rooftop. They
had landed in a huge snowdrift!

"That's not a very good start,"
said Santa as he brushed the snow
from his jacket. "We'll have to
be more careful!"
He picked up some presents that
had fallen out of the sleigh.
They set off once more. It was
still snowing very hard.
Finally, Santa had to admit
they were lost.
"We'll never deliver these
presents on time," he sighed.

They saw a wise old owl sitting in a tree. The owl blinked in surprise when he saw the sleigh, but he was able to tell Santa the way to the nearest town. "At last!" cried Santa as the rows of rooftops came into view. "Now we can make a start!" The reindeer landed softly on the first rooftop and Santa climbed down the chimney with his sack of presents.

He landed in the fireplace
and then wished he hadn't.
Someone had left a bunch of holly
there. He jumped up with it
sticking to his bottom.
"I wish people would be more
careful," he said, pulling
the holly out. "It would be so much
easier if I could come through
the front door like everyone else!"

Santa worked all through the
night, going up and down
chimneys of all shapes and sizes.
Once he got stuck. When he came
out at the bottom, his clothes were
covered with soot.
"They were clean this morning,"
he sighed.
In another house he nearly burned
his beard when he found the ashes
of a fire still hot.

"Some people do make my job
difficult," he said. "Still, there aren't
many more houses to go!"
He came to the very last house.
There he found some cake and
a glass of milk waiting for him.
"How nice," he said. "Just what
I need before I go home!"
He sat down in a chair and
started to eat the cake.

The house was warm and Santa was
very tired. It wasn't long before
he was fast asleep.
Up on the roof the reindeer began
to get worried. Santa had been
gone a long time and soon it
would start to get light.
They peered through the windows
and tapped on the glass until
Santa woke up.
"Thank you, my friends," he said.
"I must have fallen asleep!"

He climbed into the sleigh and
they set off for home. Without
the presents on board the sleigh
was much lighter. They headed
quickly back toward the snowy
lands of the north.
They arrived safely home just as
dawn was breaking.
"Well done, all of you," said Santa.
He led the reindeer back
to the stables. "I think we all
need some sleep!"

Santa awoke later that morning
feeling much better.
He remembered it was Christmas
Day. He smiled as he thought of
everyone waking up all over the
world and opening their presents.
He looked at the foot of his bed
and saw a stocking filled with
presents for himself.
''Well, imagine that,'' he said.
''Who could have given me these?
Merry Christmas, everyone!''

Say these words again

Santa Claus   careful
wrapped   elves
paint   cake
shapes   milk
ride   soot
beard   tapped
swirling   climbed

What can you see?

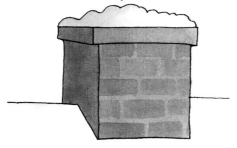

chimney

holly

milk

bells

boots

Lottie
the Littlest Reindeer

Far, far away in a northern
land covered in ice and snow,
there lived a little reindeer
called Lottie.
Lottie was much smaller than the
other reindeer and this made her
feel very shy.
"I wish I wasn't so small,"
sighed Lottie. "Then I could play
with the other reindeer."

But Lottie had another wish,
something that she wanted more
than anything else in the world.
"I wish . . . I wish I could help
pull Santa's sleigh," said Lottie.
"Maybe you will, one day,"
said her mother.
"But it is Christmas soon and
I'm so little," sighed Lottie.
"Then you must wait until you have
grown up, first," replied her mother.

The other reindeer were much
bigger than Lottie. They were
very excited at the thought of
helping Santa.
"I wonder who will be chosen to
help pull Santa's sleigh this year?"
asked one. "I think it should be
the strongest."
"No, it should be the fastest,"
called another.
"We will hold a contest,"
said a wise, old reindeer.
"That's the best way to choose
who should pull the sleigh."

Lottie had been listening to the other reindeer. This was her chance to help pull Santa's sleigh!
"May I enter the contest, too?" she asked, shyly.
"If you want to," said one reindeer. "But you'll never win. You're far too small!"

The first event was a running race. Lottie stood with the other reindeer on the starting line.
"The first two reindeer to run to that tree and back will be the winners," said the judge.
"On your marks, get set, go!" Lottie ran as fast as she could but she couldn't keep up with the others. Her legs were far too short and she watched sadly as the other reindeer ran past her.

"Perhaps I'll be better at the
next event," said Lottie and she
watched as a rope was tied
between two trees. One by one
the reindeer jumped over it.
When it was Lottie's turn
she took a long run and jumped.
Poor Lottie! Her little legs
caught on the rope and she
landed on the ground with
a big bump!
"Bad luck, Lottie!" called
the judge. "You're just too little!"

"The test of strength is my last chance," said Lottie. "If only I can win."

"This is Santa's sleigh," said the judge. "All you have to do is pull it as far as you can."

Little Lottie was tied to the sleigh. But no matter how hard she tried, she could not move it. She was so unhappy.

"Never mind," said Lottie's mother. "You can always try again next year."

The next day, the winners were
called out. Lottie watched
sadly as the six fittest and
strongest reindeer walked proudly
over to the sleigh.
It was full to the top with
presents of all shapes and sizes.
"I wish I could go, too,"
sighed Lottie. "It must be so
exciting to help Santa deliver all
the presents."

Suddenly a great cheer went up.
"Here comes Santa!" cried Lottie.
"Greetings, my friends!"
cried Santa Claus as he strode
towards them. "It's good to see
you all again!"
He quickly checked the sleigh
then tied the reindeer to it.
"We really must be going,"
said Santa smiling. "We have
a long night ahead of us!"

Lottie looked sadly at the sleigh before it set off. Then just as she was turning to go home, she saw the leading reindeer slip and fall into a snowdrift.

"Oh, no!" cried Santa.

"Now what are we going to do? There are so many presents to deliver and not enough reindeer to pull the sleigh!"

Then Santa saw a little reindeer
standing in the distance.
"Lottie!" he cried. "You are just
what we need! Will you help to pull
my sleigh?"
Lottie could hardly believe her ears.
Her special Christmas wish was
about to come true!
"Oh, yes!" she cried and the
other reindeer smiled as Lottie
was placed at the front of
Santa's sleigh. They all knew how
much Lottie wanted to help.

Lottie stood proudly at the front, her eyes shining happily.

"At last," said Santa. "Now we can deliver all the presents."

He sprinkled the reindeer with magic dust and Lottie suddenly felt lighter.

"I can fly!" she cried.

Lottie's mother watched proudly as the sleigh climbed into the air with Lottie leading the way.

What a night Lottie had!
The reindeer stopped at every
house and Santa dropped down
the chimney with his sack
of presents. At last the
reindeer arrived home
as it was getting light.
"Thank you, all!" cried Santa.
"Now everyone can wake up
to a happy Christmas!"
Then Santa smiled and said,
"And a special thank you to
Lottie, the littlest reindeer!"
Lottie had never been so happy!

Say these words again

shy	deliver
Christmas	judge
smile	jump
proudly	dark
contest	night
front	glow
race	red

What can you see?

rope

reindeer

Santa Claus

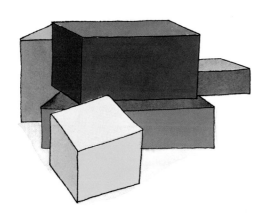

presents

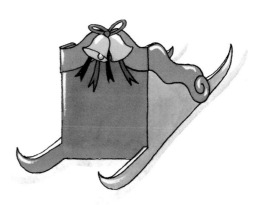

sleigh

The Hungry
Snowman

It had been snowing hard all
night. By morning the snow lay
white and deep over everything.
Sam looked out of his bedroom
window. He felt very excited.
He ran downstairs to find
his mother.
"May I go and play outside?"
he asked. "It looks great fun!"
"All right," said his mother.
"But put on your gloves and
scarf. It's very cold."

Sam ran outside and met
his friends. Soon they were
playing in the snow. They began
to throw snowballs at each other.
Then Sam said, ''Let's build
a snowman!''
''Here's some coal for his eyes,''
said Jim.
''And a carrot for his nose,''
said Jenny.
''He looks almost real,'' said Sam.
He put his scarf around the
snowman's neck.

"Dinnertime!" called Sam's
mother. Sam went back indoors.
Outside all was very quiet.
Very, very slowly the snowman began
to move. He looked around carefully
to make sure no one was about.
Then he said crossly, "It's all right
for Sam, but no one worries
about my dinner. They must know
that a snowman gets hungry too!".

103

A squirrel ran into the garden.
She was carrying some nuts.
"Hello," said the snowman.
"May I share your dinner?
I'm very hungry."
The squirrel dropped her nuts
in surprise. A talking snowman!
"You can have some nuts if you
like," she said. "They are
very nice."
"Oh dear!" said the snowman.
"They're much too hard. I cannot
eat these for my dinner."

A rabbit hopped into the garden.
"Hello," said the snowman.
"What do you eat?"
The rabbit looked at the snowman's
nose and laughed.
"I like carrots best of all!" he said.
"Oh dear!" cried the snowman.
"That's no good. I can't eat
my own nose!"
"Don't worry," said the rabbit.
"There are plenty of other things
to eat."

The snowman looked up. He saw
a robin sitting on the branch
of a tree. It was singing merrily.
"Hello," said the snowman.
"You sound happy today."
"It's because this tree is full
of juicy berries for me to eat,"
said the robin. "Why don't
you try some?"
"Oh no, I can't," said the snowman.
"Only birds can eat those.
Oh, I am so hungry. What shall I do?"

Then a wonderful smell began to
fill the air. It was coming from
the kitchen. The snowman walked
slowly across the garden.
He looked into the kitchen.
He could see Sam's mother baking
cookies and icing cakes. The sight
of them made the snowman's
mouth water.
"That's what I would like to eat!"
he cried. "I'll just have to wait
until nobody is looking!"

Later that night, when everyone was asleep, the snowman tiptoed into the kitchen. He opened the refrigerator door and found a large plate of cream cakes. "These taste wonderful!" he said, happily helping himself. "Much better than nuts and berries!" He ate some cookies. Then he ate a bowl of ice cream. Feeling much better, he crept back outside without a sound.

The next morning Sam's mother
was very surprised. All of her
cream cakes were missing.
''And someone has taken all the
cookies, too!'' she said.
''Was it you, Sam?''
''Not me,'' said Sam.
''And look at these big wet
footprints on the floor,''
she said crossly. ''Where have
they come from?''

Every night the snowman crept
into the house for his dinner.
Every morning Sam's mother
asked where her food had gone.
"First it was cream cakes and
ice cream," she said. "But now
all the cold ham and turkey
has disappeared, too!"
Sam looked at the wet footprints.
They led outside. Sam looked
at the snowman. "I'm sure he's
getting fatter," he said.

One night the snowman ate far
too much.
"I'll sit here and rest," he said.
Soon he was fast asleep. Hours
later he woke up. He was lying
in a pool of water.
"Oh no!" he cried. "I'm melting!"
He was too weak to reach
the door.
"I'll hide in the refrigerator,"
he said. "It's cold in there!"
As he climbed in, the door
slammed shut!

The next morning Sam ran out
into the garden. He couldn't
believe his eyes. His snowman
had disappeared! His mother was in
the kitchen mopping up a pool
of water.
"Something very odd is going on
here," she said. "I'll check the
refrigerator." She opened the door
and gasped in amazement. Inside
was the snowman, only he was
much, much smaller!

"How did he get in there?"
asked Sam. "Look how small he is!"
He carried the snowman outside.
"You'd better stay here from now on,"
he said, smiling. "I'll bring
out some food for you. So don't
try any more tricks."
The snowman had learned his lesson.
After his narrow escape
he decided he was much safer
outside where he belonged.
He decided never to steal food
from the kitchen again!

Say these words again

snow	nuts
deep	branch
coal	berries
carrot	cakes
scarf	wet
dinner	fatter
squirrel	smaller

Who can you see?

snowman

Sam

mother

squirrel

rabbit